THE PIANO SOLOS OF
RICHARD · CLAYDERMAN

WISE PUBLICATIONS
LONDON/NEW YORK/SYDNEY/COLOGNE

MUSIC SALES LIMITED
8/9 FRITH STREET, LONDON W1V 5TZ, ENGLAND

MUSIC SALES CORPORATION
225 PARK AVENUE SOUTH, NEW YORK, NY 10003, USA

MUSIC SALES PTY. LIMITED
120 ROTHSCHILD AVENUE, ROSEBERY, NSW 2018, AUSTRALIA

THIS BOOK   COPYRIGHT 1983 BY WISE PUBLICATIONS
ISBN 0.7119.0284.4/ORDER NO. AM 32855

BOOK DESIGNED BY HILARY SABINE

MUSIC SALES COMPLETE CATALOGUE LISTS THOUSANDS
OF TITLES AND IS FREE FROM YOUR LOCAL MUSIC
BOOK SHOP, OR DIRECT FROM MUSIC SALES LIMITED.
PLEASE SEND £1.75 IN STAMPS FOR POSTAGE TO
MUSIC SALES LIMITED, 8/9 FRITH STREET, LONDON W1V 5TZ

PRINTED IN ENGLAND BY HALSTAN & CO. LIMITED, AMERSHAM, BUCKS.

SECRET OF MY LOVE

COMPOSER · PAUL DE SENNEVILLE & OLIVIER TOUSSAINT

2 x D.S.
and Fade

5

ROMANTICA SERENADE

COMPOSER · PAUL DE SENNEVILLE & OLIVIER TOUSSAINT

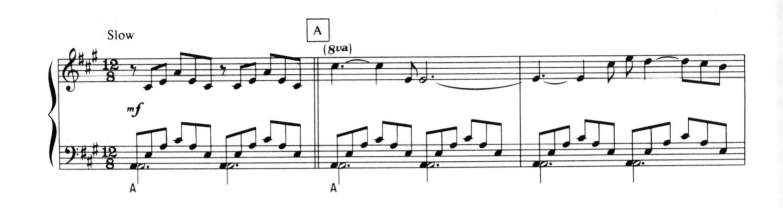

Repeat ad lib. and Fade

LETTRE A MA MERE

COMPOSER · PAUL DE SENNEVILLE

HISTOIRE D'UN REVE

COMPOSER · PAUL DE SENNEVILLE

L'Enfant Et La Mer

COMPOSER · PAUL DE SENNEVILLE & OLIVIER TOUSSAINT

REPRISE
AD LIB AND FADE.

OLD FASHION

COMPOSER · PAUL DE SENNEVILLE
AUTHOR · OLIVIER TOUSSAINT

then you gon·na sing   old   tune,   old   tune   So you gon·na make

mo·ney, mo·ney with   old   fashion,   old   fashion   so you gon·na make

mo·ney, mo·ney with   old   fashion,   old   fashion.

Repeat ad lib. *al Coda*

Coda

15

Bye Bye Tristesse

ORIGINAL COMPOSER · CHOPIN & PAUL DE SENNEVILLE
ARRANGER · OLIVIER TOUSSAINT & GERARD SALESSES

REPEAT FROM A TO B

18

REPEAT FROM C TO D

20

Bach Gammon

ORIGINAL COMPOSER · BACH, TCHAIKOVSKY, BRAHMS & PAUL DE SENNEVILLE
ARRANGER · OLIVIER TOUSSAINT & GERARD SALESSES

JARDIN SECRET

COMPOSER · PAUL DE SENNEVILLE

Ballade Pour Adeline

COMPOSER · PAUL DE SENNEVILLE

A Comme Amour

COMPOSER · PAUL DE SENNEVILLE
AUTHOR · OLIVIER TOUSSAINT

But you should say, Oh yes _____ you should come with me when

B♭m   A♭   D♭

I ask _____ you should mar - ry me when _____ I pray _____ then I'll take you in my

F7/A

arms love _____ I will press your hands a - gainst _____ a - gainst my

F7   B♭m

heart.

get   I am sure.

C7   F7

Reve D'Amour

ORIGINAL COMPOSER · LISZT
ARRANGER · OLIVIER TOUSSAINT & GERARD SALESSES

Triste Coeur

COMPOSER · PAUL DE SENNEVILLE

39

CONCERTO POUR UNE JEUNE FILLE NOMMEE 'JE T'AIME'

COMPOSER · PAUL DE SENNEVILLE

43

Souvenirs D'Enfance

COMPOSER · PAUL DE SENNEVILLE

Nostalgy

COMPOSER · OLIVIER TOUSSAINT

Mariage D'Amour

COMPOSER · PAUL DE SENNEVILLE

Melodie Des Souvenirs

COMPOSER · OLIVIER TOUSSAINT

2ND TIME TO A

11/90 (10844)